D1531668

What Hppened In
US HISTORY:

This Is a Journal Notebook **written record of incidents, experiences, and ideas**. Also known as a personal journal, notebook, diary, and log. Writers often keep journals to record observations and explore ideas that may eventually be developed into more formal essays, articles, and stories

WHAT HAPPENED IN US HISTORY THE YEAR YOU WERE BORN.

THIS JOURNAL BELONGS TO :

Name :

Address :

Phone :

QUICK REMIDER :

IF YOU FIND THIS JOURNAL
CREATIVE & USEFUL
We Would Be Very Grateful
IF You Posted a Short Review
ON « AMAZON » Your Support
Does Make a Difference And
We Read Every Review
Personaly

1920s Cost of Living :

- **Average Cost Of New House** : $6,296

- **Average Income** : $2,160 per year

- **New Car** : $525

- **Average Rent** : $15 per month

- **Movie Ticket** : 15 cents each

- **Gasoline** : 33 cents per gallon

- **First Class Postage Stamp** : $2 cents

Give Your Notes About This Event :

Sport Events:

- July : Golf British Open won by Walter Hagen

- Aug : Golf US PGA won by Gene Sarazen

- Sep :Tennis US National Championship won by Bill Tilden and Molla Mallory

- Oct : The Baseball World Series won by New York Giants

Give Your Notes About This Event :

Popular Culture :

- **Jazz music** became wildly popular in the "Roaring Twenties," a decade that witnessed unprecedented economic growth and prosperity in the United States. Consumer culture flourished, with ever greater numbers of Americans purchasing automobiles, electrical appliances, and other widely available consumer products.

Give Your Notes About This Event :

Economy:

-There were several interruptions to this growth. In mid-1920 the American economy began to contract and the 1920-1921 depression lasted about a year, but a rapid recovery reestablished full-employment by 1923. As will be discussed below, the Federal Reserve System's monetary policy was a major factor in initiating the 1920-1921 depression. From 1923 through 1929 growth was much smoother. There was a very mild recession in 1924 and another mild recession in 1927 both of which may be related to oil price shocks (McMillin and Parker, 1994). The 1927 recession was also associated with Henry Ford's shut-down of all his factories for six months in order to changeover from the Model T to the new Model A automobile. Though the Model T's market share was declining after 1924, in 1926 Ford's Model T still made up nearly 40 percent of all the new cars produced and sold in the United States. The Great Depression began in the summer of 1929, possibly as early as June. The initial downturn was relatively mild but the contraction accelerated after the crash of the stock market at the end of October. Real total GNP fell 10.2 percent from 1929 to 1930 while real GNP per capita fell 11.5 percent from 1929 to 1930.

Give Your Notes About This Event :

Important Events:

1. THE LEAGUE OF NATIONS WAS ESTABLISHED IN 1920.

2. AMERICA HAD A DE-FACTO WOMAN PRESIDENT

.

3. THE U.S. SUSTAINED WHAT WAS THEN ITS WORST TERRORIST ATTACK IN

4. J. EDGAR HOOVER BEGAN HIS ASCENT

5. WOMEN GAINED THE RIGHT TO VOTE

Give Your Notes About This Event :

Technology:

-The Electric Automatic Traffic Signal

-Quick-Frozen Food

-Water Skis

-Television

-While the Great Depression is felt at every level in the workforce, the period is one of great innovation and development of new materials and technology.

Give Your Notes About This Event :

1920s US HISTORY

1920s US HISTORY

1920s US HISTORY

1920s US HISTORY

1920s US HISTORY

1920s US HISTORY

1920s US HISTORY

1920s US HISTORY

1920s US HISTORY

1920s US HISTORY

1920s US HISTORY

1920s US HISTORY

1920s US HISTORY

1920s US HISTORY

1920s US HISTORY

1920s US HISTORY

1920s US HISTORY

1920s US HISTORY

1920s US HISTORY

1920s US HISTORY

1920s US HISTORY

1920s US HISTORY

1920s US HISTORY

1920s US HISTORY

1920s US HISTORY

1920s US HISTORY

1920s US HISTORY

1920s US HISTORY

1920s US HISTORY

1920s US HISTORY

1920s US HISTORY

1920s US HISTORY

1920s US HISTORY

1920s US HISTORY

1920s US HISTORY

1920s US HISTORY

1920s US HISTORY

1920s US HISTORY

1920s US HISTORY

1920s US HISTORY

1920s US HISTORY

1920s US HISTORY

1920s US HISTORY

1920s US HISTORY

1920s US HISTORY

1920s US HISTORY

1920s US HISTORY

1920s US HISTORY

1920s US HISTORY

1920s US HISTORY

1920s US HISTORY

1920s US HISTORY

1920s US HISTORY

1920s US HISTORY

1920s US HISTORY

1920s US HISTORY

1920s US HISTORY

1920s US HISTORY

1920s US HISTORY

1920s US HISTORY

1920s US HISTORY

1920s US HISTORY

1920s US HISTORY

1920s US HISTORY

1920s US HISTORY

1920s US HISTORY

1920s US HISTORY

1920s US HISTORY

1920s US HISTORY

1920s US HISTORY

1920s US HISTORY

1920s US HISTORY

1920s US HISTORY

1920s US HISTORY

1920s US HISTORY

1920s US HISTORY

1920s US HISTORY

1920s US HISTORY

1920s US HISTORY

1920s US HISTORY

1920s US HISTORY

1920s US HISTORY

1920s US HISTORY

1920s US HISTORY

1920s US HISTORY

Made in the USA
Columbia, SC
21 February 2022

56584599R00057